BOOK 2

Piano Literature

of the 17th, 18th and 19th Centuries

The five volumes of the *Piano Literature* series (Books 2, 3, 4, 5, 6) contain a selection of choice smaller keyboard works in original form by master composers of the 17th, 18th and 19th centuries. As the best introduction to this literature, the editors have chosen well-known folk songs, piano arrangements of which are presented in Book 1.

In making the selections, the editors were careful to consider the technical and musical readiness of the average student at each level and to maintain uniformity of difficulty throughout each volume.

The series aims to provide:

1) The necessary technical and musical preparation for performance of the composers' major works, through experience with representative lesser works at each grade level.

2) Experience in a variety of styles and forms and an understanding of the way these styles and forms have developed in the history of music.

Selected and Correlated by Frances Clark

Edited by Louise Goss

D1413791

Cover Design: Debbie Johns

© 1954 Summy-Birchard Music
division of Summy-Birchard, Inc.
Exclusive print rights administered by
Alfred Music Publishing Co., Inc.
All Rights Reserved.   Printed in USA.

ISBN-10: 0-87487-126-3
ISBN-13: 987-0-87487-126-5

Johann Sebastian Bach
1685–1750

*J*OHANN SEBASTIAN BACH was the best-known member of a famous musical family. He lived all of his life in a section of Germany that in those days was called Thuringia.

As a young boy, Bach took music lessons from a number of fine teachers. One of them was his own older brother, with whom he lived after his parents died. Bach had a fine boy-soprano voice and learned to play the violin, harpsichord*, clavichord* and organ.

As a young man, he was well known in his own country as a teacher, organist and conductor. It was not until many years after his death that people all over the world came to realize what a great *composer* he had been. In 1950 the whole world honored him on the two hundredth anniversary of his death.

Bach was one of the busiest musicians who ever lived. He gave lessons on the instruments that he had learned to play as a boy; he taught singing, and even Latin, to schoolboys; he directed choirs and small orchestras; he copied (by hand) almost all of the music he used; and he even tuned and repaired his own musical instruments! Yet, no matter how busy he was, he always found time for composing and wrote music both for the church and for the court.

An important part of his music was for keyboard instruments—organ, harpsichord and clavichord. The harpsichord and clavichord were keyboard instruments somewhat like the piano, which were popular before the piano was invented. Even though the piano was invented during Bach's lifetime (in 1709), he played one only a few times and never composed any music for it. Today, since harpsichords and clavichords are uncommon, we play his music on the piano.

Bach did not write very much keyboard music for young students. The four pieces in this collection are not actually by Bach himself and are simpler than anything he composed. They are part of a music notebook[1] that Bach and his wife, Anna Magdalena, prepared for their own children's music lessons. We do not know the names of the composers of the four pieces in our collection, but we do know that they were popular in Bach's day and that his children learned to play them.

---

[1] This notebook has come to be known as the *Anna Magdalena Bach Notebook*. It includes many pieces by Bach and some by other composers.

*Bourrée

Allegro (♩ = about 132)

From the "Anna Magdalena
Bach Notebook"

Minuet

Moderato (♩ = about 126)

From the "Anna Magdalena
Bach Notebook"

Minuet

Andante con moto (♩ = about 120)

From the "Anna Magdalena
Bach Notebook"

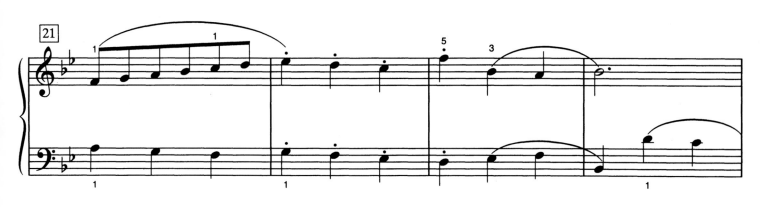

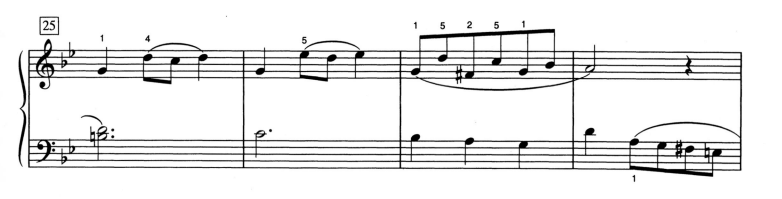

Musette

Con brio (♩ = about 88)

From the "Anna Magdalena
Bach Notebook"

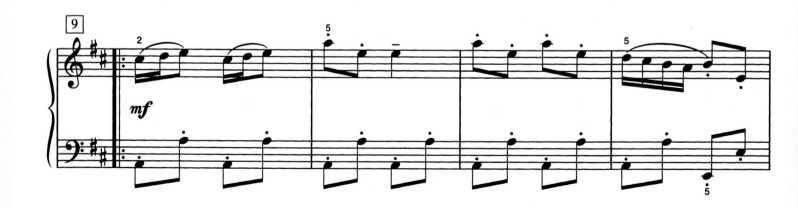

Leopold Mozart
1719–1787

*L*EOPOLD MOZART was born in the German village of Augsburg, where his father was a poor bookbinder. He learned music as a choirboy and as a violin student. When he was a young man, Leopold went to Salzburg, where he studied first religion and then law. But his greatest interest was always music, and before long he gave up the idea of being a priest or lawyer and decided to become a musician.

Mozart was well known in his own country as a composer of oratorios*, operas*, symphonies* and piano music. He was famous all over Europe, too, as the composer of an instruction book for violin students called *The Violin School*.

But, of course, it is as the father of one of the greatest composers who ever lived that we remember him best today. This famous son, Wolfgang Amadeus Mozart, was born in 1756.

As a surprise for Wolfgang's seventh birthday, Leopold prepared a book of piano pieces, which is known as the *Little Music Book for Wolfgang*. The pieces in this book were not actually by Leopold himself but were compositions that he selected and arranged for Wolfgang to study.

Minuet

Con moto (♩ = about 144)

From Leopold Mozart's
"Notebook for Wolfgang"

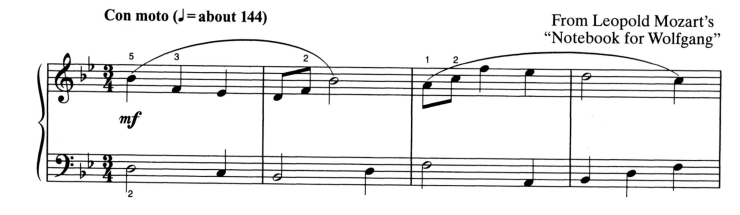

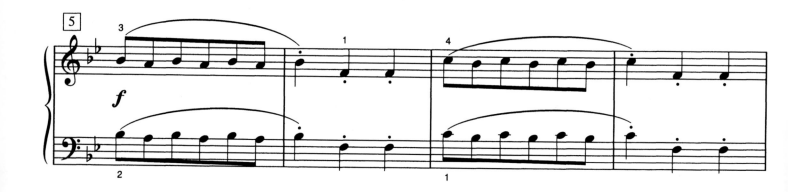

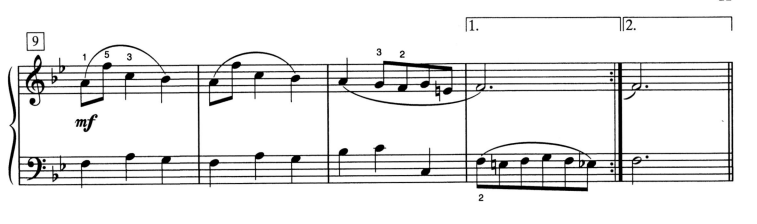

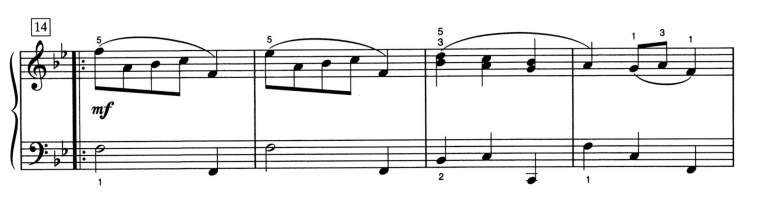

(Franz) Joseph Haydn
1732–1809

*J*OSEPH HAYDN was born in the village of Rohrau, in a part of Austria that is very near to Hungary.

Haydn was a poor peasant boy. His father was a wagon-maker and his mother a cook. Though his parents loved music, no one in his family had ever been a musician.

As a young boy, Haydn went to live with a cousin in a nearby town. This cousin was a school master and musician and became Haydn's first music teacher. Joseph learned to play the violin and harpsichord and also studied singing, and soon he became the favorite soloist in the church choir.

When Haydn was eight, the music director of a great church in Vienna heard him sing and invited him to join the St. Stephen's choir school and choir. There he learned more about music and began to teach himself how to compose.

As a young man, he continued to live in Vienna and study music. He made a small income by teaching, accompanying and playing in orchestras. In those days Vienna was one of the great musical centers of Europe, and Haydn met many of the finest composers and musicians of the time.

For a short time, Haydn was music director at an Austrian court, but soon he became music director for Prince Esterházy in Hungary, a position he held for almost thirty years. Prince Esterházy had one of the most splendid courts in all of Europe, and Haydn's job was to provide musical entertainment for the prince and his guests. He was kept busy from morning until night, directing the choir and orchestra; putting on operas, operettas and puppet shows; and composing. A great deal of the music the choir and orchestra performed was by Haydn. He wrote every kind of music popular at that time—music for orchestra, chamber music*, piano music, choral music, songs, church music and operas.

Although he lived so many years at the lavish Esterházy palace, Haydn's music never lost its freshness and simplicity. It was always full of fun and bubbling with merriment, as simple and natural as the peasant tunes he had heard as a boy. Some of the simplest and most cheerful music he wrote was for dancing. Among his piano pieces are dozens of bright, colorful dances like those in this collection.

Minuet

Andante (♩ = about 108)

Joseph Haydn

German Dances

15

Giocoso (♩ = about 152)

No. 3 (1)

(1) Originally written in the key of E Major.

0126

Quadrille

Con brio (♪ = about 132)

Joseph Haydn

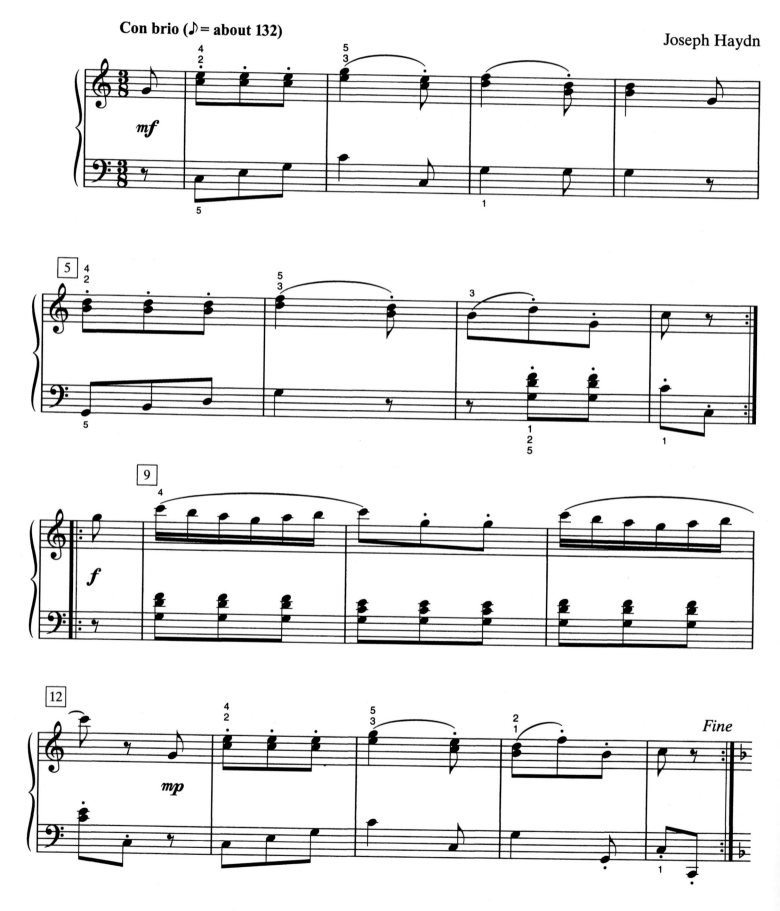

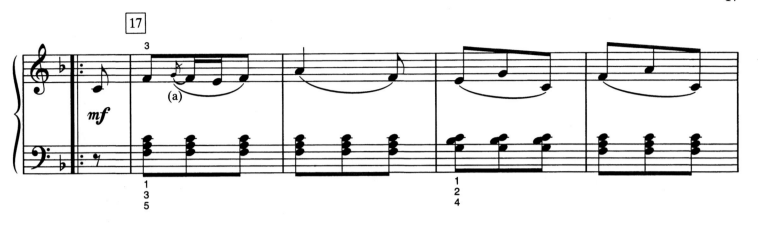

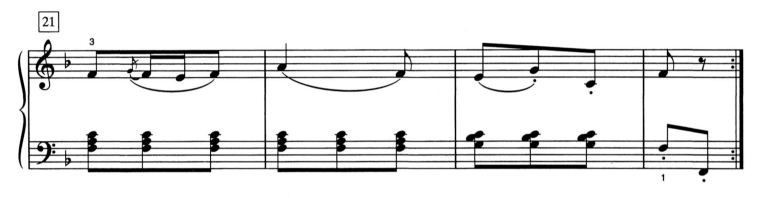

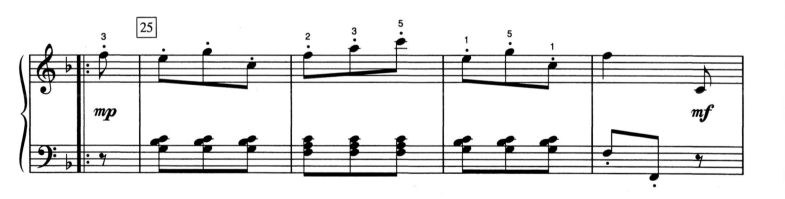

D.C. al Fine

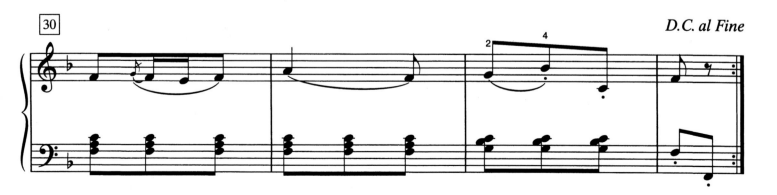

(a) When ornamental notes are not written out, they are to be played as *grace notes.

Wolfgang Amadeus Mozart
1756–1791

WOLFGANG AMADEUS MOZART has often been called the wonder boy of music. His father was Leopold Mozart, a well-known violinist and composer. Leopold began to give Wolfgang music lessons when he was only four years old and on his seventh birthday gave him the *Little Music Book for Wolfgang* (see pages 10 and 11).

As a child, Wolfgang learned to play the violin, organ, harpsichord and piano. The piano was always his favorite instrument, and he became one of the outstanding pianists of his time. He began to write music when he was only five years old, and the very first pieces he wrote were for piano.

By the time he was six, Wolfgang was already such a fine pianist, violinist and composer that his father took him and his older sister on a tour. They visited Munich and Vienna, and everyone who heard them was amazed by the children and their music. In the next ten years they visited Paris, London and Italy, playing for kings and queens and for the most famous musicians of the time. Everyone thought that Mozart would some day become a great musician.

As a young man, Mozart lived in Salzburg, where he and his father were both musicians for the Archbishop. Later he moved to Vienna, where he became an opera and symphony composer.

Mozart lived only thirty-five years, but in his short lifetime he wrote more than six hundred compositions—operas, symphonies, chamber music, choral works, songs and a great deal of piano music. Ever since his death, people all over the world have played and loved his music.

The *Minuet* and *Allegro* included in this collection were written in Salzburg when Mozart was six years old.

Minuet, K. 2

Grazioso (♩ = about 144)

Wolfgang Amadeus Mozart

Allegro, K. 3

Allegro moderato (♩ = about 120)

Wolfgang Amadeus Mozart

Ludwig van Beethoven
1770–1827

*L*UDWIG VAN BEETHOVEN was a member of a poor but musical family. His grandfather was a fine bass singer and opera composer and became the chapel master for the elector of Cologne.

Beethoven's father was a tenor singer and was also a musician at the elector's court. Like Mozart, Beethoven began to take music lessons from his father when he was only four years old. The other court musicians also helped give Ludwig lessons, and he soon learned to play the violin, organ and piano.

When Beethoven was six, he gave his first piano concert in Cologne. By the time he was eight, he could also play the violin very well. This reminded his father of the young Mozart, so he encouraged Beethoven to work hard and practice faithfully in the hope that he would become a second Mozart.

At the age of eleven, Beethoven was already an excellent pianist, and it is probable that he made a short tour through Holland, playing for musicians and noblemen, just as Mozart had done when he was a young boy. When he was twelve, he joined his father and grandfather as a musician in the elector's court in Cologne. He was given the job of assistant organist in the court chapel and sometimes played violin in the court orchestra.

The elector realized that Beethoven would some day become a fine musician and, when the young composer was seventeen, sent him to Vienna to study. Beethoven met and played for Mozart, and later on, when he settled permanently in Vienna, he studied for a time with Haydn. Both Haydn and Mozart praised him and predicted that he would have a great career in music.

In Vienna, Beethoven first became known as a pianist. He played in many of the great homes and also gave public concerts. Although Beethoven did not have a regular position at a court or church, several wealthy men who admired his music helped support him all of his life. When he died, twenty thousand people attended his funeral, and the greatest people of Vienna and the most famous musicians of his time paid him tribute.

All of his life Beethoven was busy composing music for orchestra, chorus and solo instruments. Some of his most beautiful music is for the piano, and the selections given here are typical of his many compositions for piano students.

Écossaise

Allegramente (♩ = about 104)

Ludwig van Beethoven

Russian Folk Song
Op. 107, No. 3(1)

Vivace (♩ = about 120)

Ludwig van Beethoven

(1) Opus 107 is a set of 10 national folk songs arranged by Beethoven for violin and piano. The examples given here are in each case the original statement of the theme as played by the instruments in unison.

Russian Folk Song
Op. 107, No. 7

Moderato con moto (♩ = about 96)

Ludwig van Beethoven

Sonatina In G

Ludwig van Beethoven

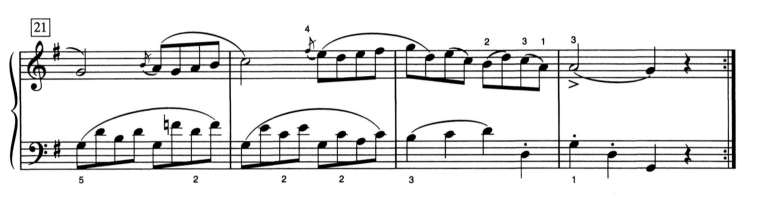

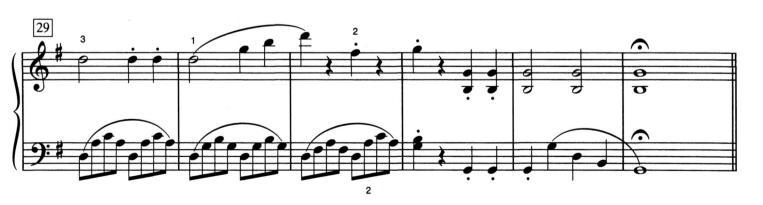

28

Romanze (♩. = about 72)

0126

Robert Schumann
1810–1856

*R*OBERT SCHUMANN was born in the city of Zwickau in a part of Germany known as Saxony. His father made his living by writing books and running a bookstore, but he was also very interested in music. The Schumanns had many musical friends, and their home was often filled with music.

Schumann began to take piano lessons when he was eight years old, and by the time he was eleven he was already composing. But this "music-making" was just for fun, and for a long while it didn't occur to him that he might some day become a musician.

Both his father and mother wanted Schumann to be a lawyer. When he was eighteen, he was sent to the University of Leipzig and later to the University of Heidelberg to study law. But all the while he was growing more and more interested in music.

Finally he persuaded his mother to let him give up the idea of becoming a lawyer so that he could spend all of his time learning to be a pianist. Unfortunately, after just a short time, Schumann hurt his hand and finally had to give up piano study. But not music! He decided to become a composer.

For the rest of his life he was busy composing music and writing articles about the music and musicians of his day. Mendelssohn, Liszt, Chopin and Brahms were all his friends, and the newspaper articles he wrote about their music helped people understand and enjoy it.

Although Schumann wrote symphonies, chamber music, choral music and more than two hundred songs, he is perhaps best known for his piano music. In addition to many difficult compositions, he wrote a whole book of short pieces just for students. He called it *Album for the Young*, and "The Soldier's March" is taken from this album.

Soldier's March
from "Album for the Young," Op. 68

Alla marcia (♩ = about 122)

Robert Schumann

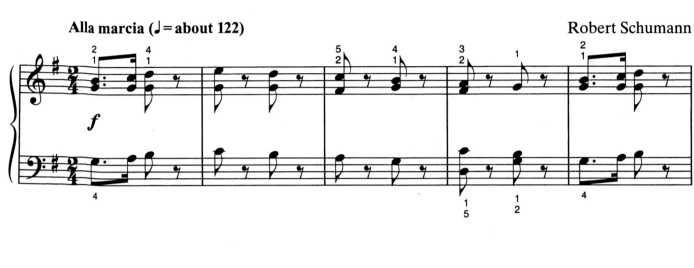

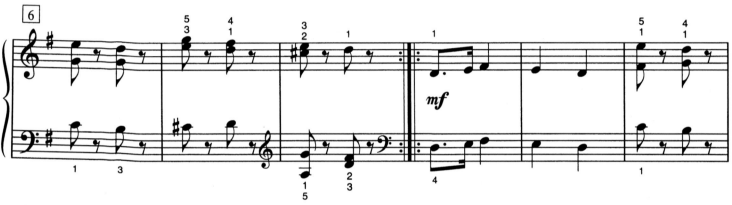

Glossary

accelerando. (*accel.*) Getting gradually faster.

accent. (>) A sudden stress or emphasis of one tone that makes it stand out from others.

accompaniment. The less important part that provides musical background for a more important part, as when a pianist accompanies a singer.

alla breve. (¢) A tempo indication for 2/2 time.

alla marcia. In march style.

allegramente. Joyfully.

allegretto. Light and cheerful, but not as quick as allegro.

allegro. Quick, lively; usually cheerful.

andante. A tempo between allegretto and adagio; flowing easily and gracefully.

appoggiatura. An extra note added above or below a melody note; it is written before the beat like this:

but played on the beat like this:

a tempo. In time; indicates a return to the original tempo after a ritardando or accelerando.

bourrée. A rapid French dance in 2/4 4/4 2/2 or ¢ time.

cantabile. In a singing manner.

chamber music. Instrumental music performed by one player to each part; different from orchestral music in which there are many players to each part.

clavichord. The earliest type of stringed keyboard instrument; a forerunner of the piano.

con brio. With spirit.

con moto. With motion.

crescendo. (*Cresc.*) ◁ Getting gradually louder.

da capo al fine. (*D.C. al fine*) A sign that means to repeat the piece from the beginning to the place marked *fine*.

descrendo. (*Decresc.*) ▷ Getting gradually softer.

diminuendo. (*Dimin.* or *dim.*) Getting gradually softer.

dolce. Sweet and soft.

écossaise. A Scottish dance in quick 2/4 time.

fermata. (⌒) A pause or hold. The sign appears over the note or rest that is to be sustained.

fine. The end.

forte. (*f*) Loud.

giocoso. Playful.

grace note. An extra note added above or below the written note:

In music from Bach through Beethoven, the grace note is played very quickly at the beginning of the beat *on* the beat; after Beethoven, it is generally played as quickly as possible, just *before* the beat.

grazioso. Graceful.

harpsichord. The keyboard instrument most popular before the piano was invented. The harpsichord tone is made by the action of tiny picks that pluck the strings, whereas the piano tone is made by the action of hammers that strike the strings.

marcato. Emphasized.

mezzo forte. (*mf*)

mezzo piano. (*mp*) Medium-soft.

minuet. A moderately slow, stately dance in 3/4 time.

moderato. In moderate tempo.

musette. Literally means bagpipe; sometimes refers to a composition, usually dance-like, with a droning accompaniment.

number. (*No.*) An individual piece, several of which make up a work or opus.

opus. (*Op.*) Work; used by composers to show in what order their works were written.

oratorio. A large work for vocal soloists, chorus and orchestra based on a religious text arranged like a drama; unlike opera, however, oratorio is not presented with costumes, scenery or stage action.

piano. (*p*) Soft.

quadrille. A French dance, the music for which was often chosen from popular tunes.

ritardando. (*Ritard.* or *rit.*) Getting gradually slower.

romanze. A slow, lyric instrumental piece.

semplice. Simple.

sforzando. (*sf* or *sfz*) A sudden or strong accent on a single note or chord.

sonata. A composition for a solo instrument (piano, violin with piano accompaniment, etc.) in three or four movements, generally in this order: Allegro, Adagio, Scherzo (or Minuet), Allegro.

sonatina. A little sonata, with fewer and shorter movements.

suite. An instrumental work made up of several dance movements all in the same key.

symphony. A large work for orchestra, generally in four movements.

vivace. Animated; quick, lively.